Je m'appelle Sophie

1ère Partie, Unité 2

Barbara Scanes

4

7

Vocabulaire

ça va ?	how are you?/are you OK?/how are things?
ça va	I'm fine/things are fine
bien	well/fine
ça va bien	I'm very well
merci	thank you
comment t'appelles-tu ?	what's your name?
je m'appelle ...	my name is...
et toi ?	and you?
ça va mal	I'm not well/things are bad
maman arrive	mum's coming
au revoir	goodbye

Luc et Sophie – a challenge

Colour in the picture and write what you think Luc and Marc are saying in the speech bubbles. (This page may be photocopied.)

Je m'appelle Sophie

Barbara Scanes

Luc and Sophie go to the park with maman. Luc sees a boy playing football. They quickly find out each other's names and start to play together. What happens when Sophie wants to join in their game?

Je m'appelle Sophie is one of the stories in *Learn French with Luc et Sophie*, a story-based scheme for teaching French in primary schools.

Full details of the scheme can be found on:
www.brilliantpublications.co.uk

ISBN-13: 978-1-78317-149-1

9 781783 171491

Brilliant
PUBLICATIONS